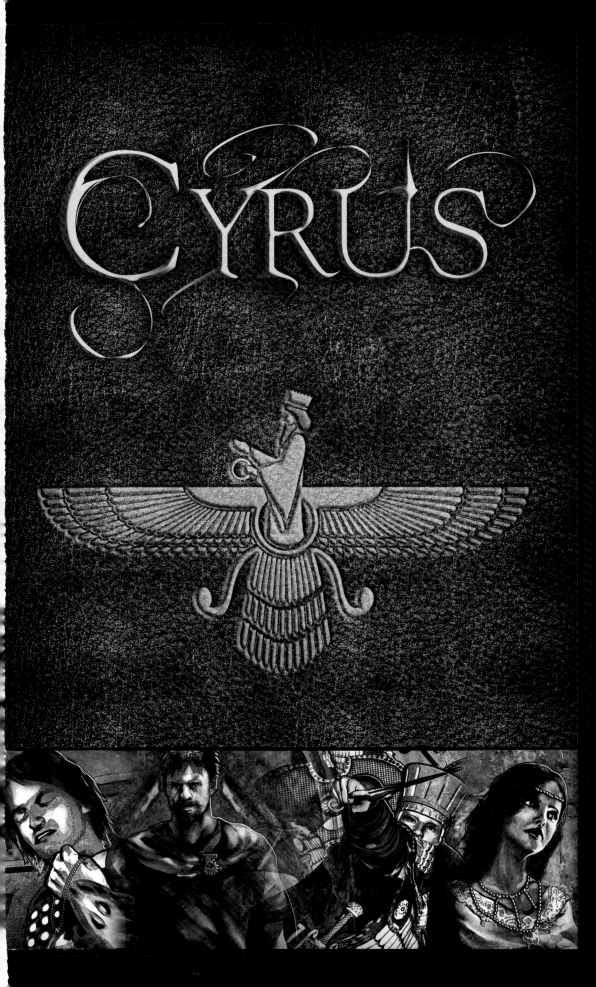

Writer and Producer
**KEI KIANPOOR**

Artist
**JASON MOSER**

Lettering
**DERON BENNETT**
with Jason Moser and Jim Spivey

Editors
**JIM SPIVEY /** Working Vacation Studios
**DAN CRISSMAN**

Cover Design
**CELIA FULLER**

Based on a screenplay by
**KEI KIANPOOR**

Screenplay Editor
**TIMOTHY HUDDLESTON**

Special Thanks to
**DANESH BALSARA**

ISBN 978-0-578-65472-0

Printed in Canada.

"Darkness cannot drive out darkness; only light can do that. Hate cannot drive out hate; only love can do that."

— Martin Luther King, Jr.

~ CHAPTER I ~
PROPHECY OF THE
NIGHTMARE

MACEDON, 344 B.C.

SPEAKING THE TRUTH, THINKING THE TRUTH, ACTING THE TRUTH, AND THE WORSHIP OF THE LIGHT ARE BIZARRE FOLLIES.

Writer and Producer:
KEI KIANPOOR

Artist:
JASON MOSER

PUBLISHED BY KRYATOR INC.

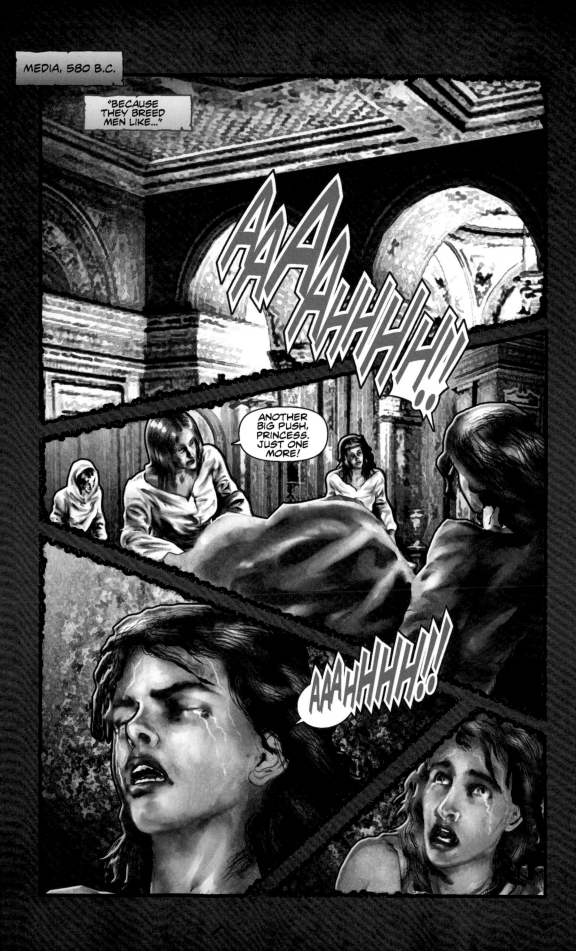

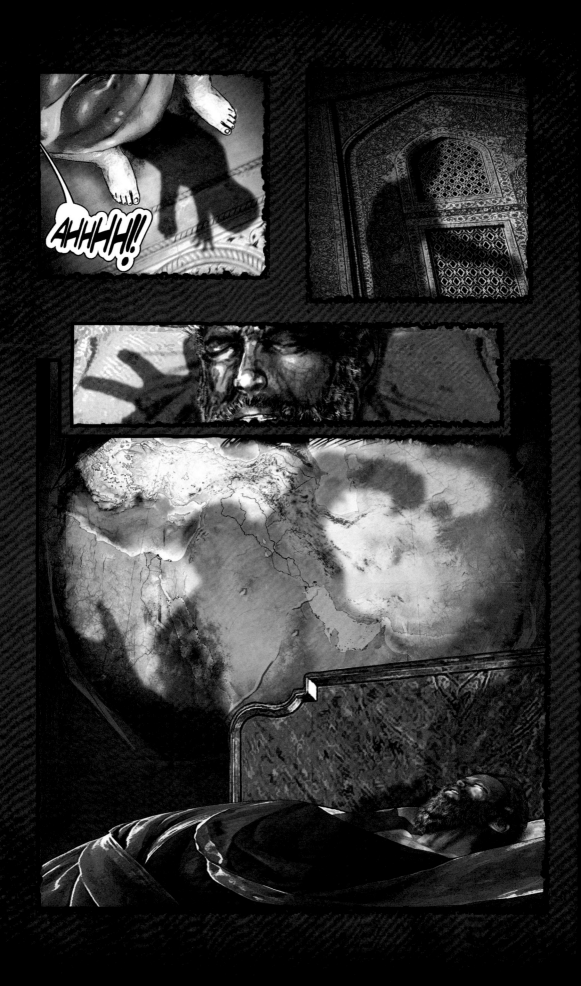

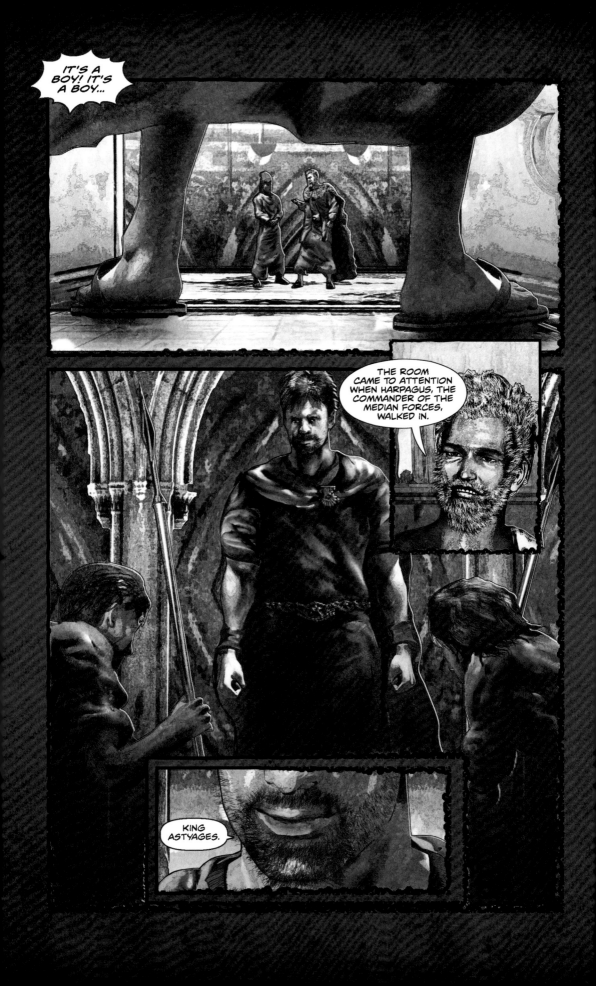

"OR WORSE, TO EAT MEAT FROM AN ANIMAL KILLED BY WOLVES AND BECOME A BLOODTHIRSTY VAMPIRE."

THE ANCIENT GREEKS BELIEVED THAT EATING THE MEAT OF WOLF-KILLED PREY WOULD TURN ONE INTO A VAMPIRE.

"PERHAPS IT WAS HIS DAYS WITH THE WOLVES THAT GAVE CYRUS SUCH AN INSTINCT FOR LEADERSHIP--"

"--AND THE COURAGE TO STAND HIS GROUND."

"ONE CAN ONLY WONDER EXACTLY WHAT CYRUS FELT FOR THE WOLF THAT HAD SUCKLED HIM AND CARED FOR HIM WHEN HE NEEDED IT MOST. BUT IF THERE'S ONE THING I'M CERTAIN OF, IT'S THAT THE DEATH OF HIS WOLF MOTHER CHANGED THE BOY FOREVER."

~ CHAPTER II ~
FOR NEDA

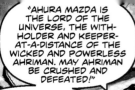

"AHURA MAZDA IS THE LORD OF THE UNIVERSE, THE WITH-HOLDER AND KEEPER-AT-A-DISTANCE OF THE WICKED AND POWERLESS AHRIMAN. MAY AHRIMAN BE CRUSHED AND DEFEATED!"

"MAY AHRIMAN, DAEVAS, DRUJAS, SORCERERS, WICKED ONES, KIKS, KARAPS, TYRANTS, SINNERS, ASHMOGHS, IMPIOUS ONES, ENEMIES, AND WITCHES BE CRUSHED AND DEFEATED."

!

MASTER, THESE ARE MY FAVORITE LINES. MAY I READ THEM?

AH, YES.

YES.

"MAY THE WICKED RULERS OF THE WORLD CEASE TO EXIST!"

"MAY THE TYRANTS BE CONFOUNDED! MAY THE ENEMIES PERISH AND CEASE TO EXIST."

"CYRUS WOULD HAVE CERTAINLY TAKEN AN ARROW IN THE EYE THAT DAY..."

"WERE IT NOT FOR THE CONSTANT VIGIL OF HIS FAMILY..."

~ CHAPTER III ~
RISE OF THE EMPIRE

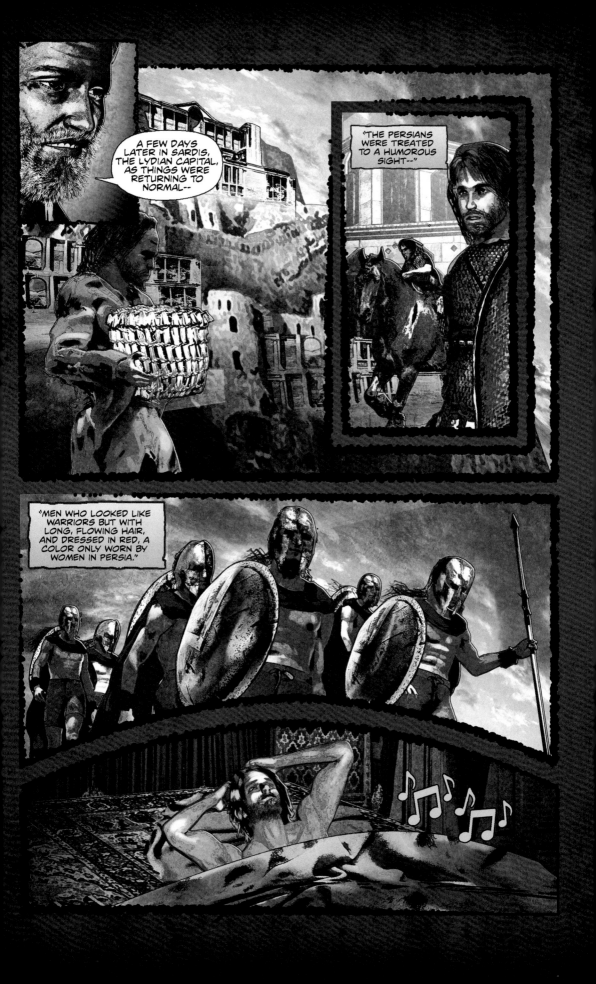

~ CHAPTER IV ~
RETURN OF THE LIGHT

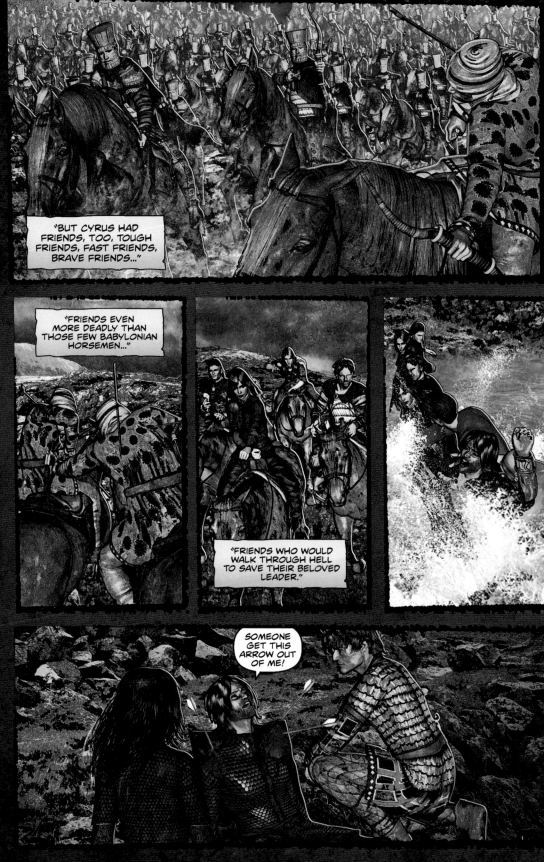

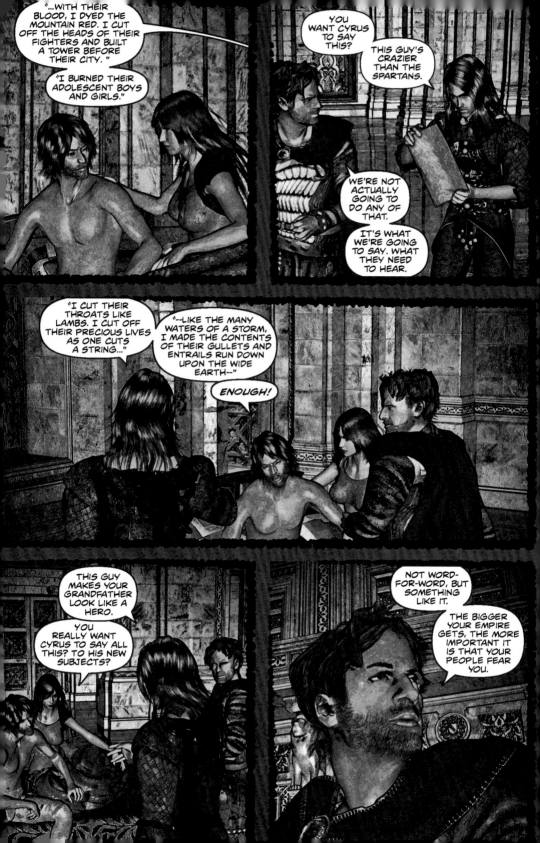

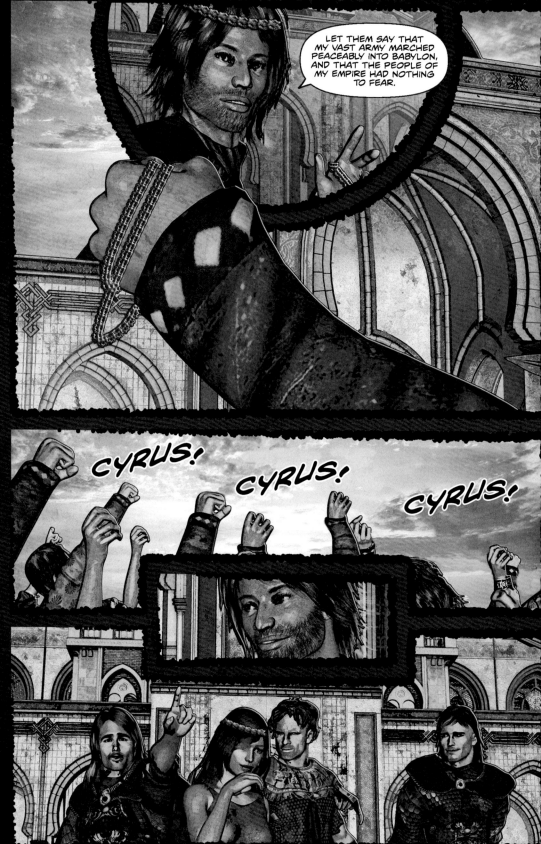

THE GREAT ITALIAN POLITICAL THEORIST, *MACHIAVELLI,* BELIEVED THAT--

Il Principe

--CYRUS WAS THE FIRST KNOWN RULER TO USE LOVE, NOT FEAR, AS THE DRIVING FORCE OF HIS EMPIRE.

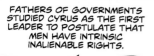

FATHERS OF GOVERNMENTS STUDIED CYRUS AS THE FIRST LEADER TO POSTULATE THAT MEN HAVE INTRINSIC INALIENABLE RIGHTS.

CYROPEDIA

CYRUS INSPIRED THEM IN THEIR OWN FIGHTS FOR THE FREEDOM OF THEIR FELLOW MEN.

HE WAS THE FIRST TO DECREE THAT EVERY INDIVIDUAL, NO MATTER WHAT HIS CREED AND COLOR, MUST BE RESPECTED UNDER THE LAW.

AS PROPHESIED IN THE OLD TESTAMENT, CYRUS FREED THE JEWS FROM THEIR BABYLONIAN CAPTIVITY AND PROVIDED THEM WITH THE MONEY TO RETURN TO THEIR LANDS, AND TO REBUILD THEIR TEMPLE.

A REPLICA OF THE CYLINDER RECORDING HIS SPEECH IN BABYLON IS ON DISPLAY IN THE HALL OF NATIONS, AS THE FIRST DECLARATION OF THE RIGHTS OF MEN.

THE ORIGINAL, DISCOVERED MORE THAN 130 YEARS AGO IN THE RUINS OF BABYLON, IS ON DISPLAY AT THE BRITISH MUSEUM.

AS YOU WELL KNOW, MY PRINCE, BABYLON WAS NOT THE WAR THAT ENDED ALL WARS. FULFILLING ASTYAGES'S WORST NIGHTMARES, CYRUS'S SHADOW EVENTUALLY SPREAD OVER A VAST EMPIRE, THE GREATEST THE WORLD HAS EVER SEEN.

"CYRUS DIED IN BATTLE AFTER PERSONALLY LEADING HIS MEN AGAINST BARBARIANS WHO HAD RAIDED VILLAGES IN THE FAR REACHES OF HIS EMPIRE..."

"BARBARIANS SO FEARSOME, THEY DRANK WINE OUT OF THE SKULLS OF THEIR SLAIN ENEMIES."

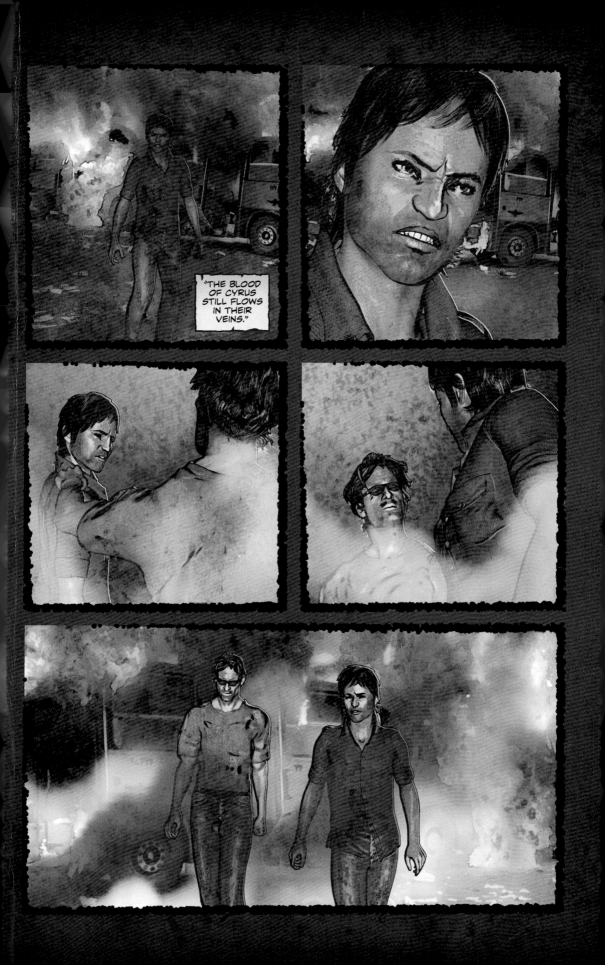

"THE BLOOD OF CYRUS STILL FLOWS IN THEIR VEINS."

"AND IT WILL SURELY RISE, AGAINST ALL ODDS, TO BATTLE CRUELTY AND INJUSTICE AGAIN."